KT-479-950

...se at home!

Contains
SERIOUSLY SCIENCEY
experiments

WARNING: Some MESSY
stuff inside. Ask a grown-up

ACC. No: 07048555

BY **JANE CLARKE** ILLUSTRATED BY **JAMES BROWN**

L'S AWESOME SCIENCE

Blast-off!

 FIVE QUILLS

Mrs Good

Mr Good

Precious

← Also starring these guys!

To Helen, who helps sort out the science! – J.C.

For Ian, Toni, Thomas and Benji x – J.B.

AL'S AWESOME SCIENCE: BLAST-OFF!

First published in Great Britain in 2018 by Five Quills
93 Oakwood Court, London W14 8JZ

www.fivequills.co.uk

Five Quills is a trademark of Five Quills

Text copyright © Five Quills 2018
Illustrations copyright © Five Quills 2018

Edited by Natascha Biebow at Blue Elephant Storyshaping
Designed by Becky Chilcott

All rights reserved. No part of this publication may be reproduced,
stored in or introduced to a retrieval system, or transmitted, in any form
or by any means (electronic, mechanical, photocopying, recording or
otherwise), without the prior written permission of the publisher.

A CIP record for this title is available from the British Library

ISBN 978 0 993553 75 2

1 3 5 7 9 10 8 6 4 2

Printed and bound in Great Britain by Clays Ltd, Elcograf S.p.A

MIX
Paper from
responsible sources
FSC® C018072
FSC
www.fsc.org

CONTENTS

Ready to Pop!

Al's experiment had begun. How many puffs would it take to fill a balloon? He took a deep breath and blew into a red one with all his might. His best friend Mia and his dog Einstein watched curiously as Al's cheeks puffed up and his freckly face went purple with the effort. The balloon just wouldn't inflate.

"Guuurgh!" Al gasped.

Einstein sighed deeply and resumed scratching his side with his back paw. He seemed to be having trouble reaching an itch.

"Try stretching the rubber first," Al's twin sister Lottie advised him. "We're not having any trouble with our balloons, are we, Filip?"

"I can blow one up in five breaths!" Lottie's best friend Filip grinned. They waved their inflated balloons at Al.

"You did my experiment!" Al sighed. "We need to catch up, Mia. There are hundreds more to blow up before the party."

Mia's eyes lit up. Al recognised the look. Mia was always doing mathematical calculations.

"800. That's how many balloons we need to fill the whole room!" Mia exclaimed excitedly.

Just then, the door opened and the twins' mum came in. "If you fill the kitchen with 800 balloons, there'll be no space for me to make the birthday cake," Mrs Boffin said. She took out a mixing bowl and set it down on the kitchen table next to her measuring scales. "I hope you haven't used up any of my ingredients for your science experiments," she muttered, reaching for the flour, sugar, icing sugar and baking powder. She opened the fridge door to get the eggs.

"We finished our egg-speriments ages and ages ago," Al assured her.

"It wasn't that long ago," Lottie said. "You always exaggerate."

"I don't!' said Al. "I'm a scientist. Scientists are accurate!"

"Not that accurate," Lottie said. "We only have two packets of balloons to blow up. That's 50 balloons, not hundreds!"

"Is that all?" Mia sounded a bit disappointed.

Filip turned to Mrs Boffin, who was busy measuring out ingredients. "What sort of cake are you making?" he asked.

"The same sponge cake I always

make every year for everyone's birthday," the twins' mum replied.

"Lottie showed me your family photos," Filip said with a smile. "It must have been fun to have three birthdays on one day."

Al and Lottie glanced at one another. Their dad's birthday was the same day as theirs, but he had died when they were small, and sometimes Mum was still sad about that. Filip was one of the few people who talked about it.

"Yes, it was great fun!" Mum agreed.

"Then we must take a photo of today's birthday fun," Filip went on.

"I was thinking that!" Mum laid down her wooden spoon and rummaged in her handbag. "This is Al and Lottie's dad's old digital camera.

I've charged it up for you to use, Filip.
Lottie says you take great photos."

"Thank you. I will do my best to
take funny ones." Filip took the camera
and pointed it at Einstein. He paused
mid-scratch with his leg in the air. He
slowly toppled over. **CLICK!**

Filip showed everyone the photo he had taken.

"You'd make a good wildlife photographer," Lottie giggled.

"We'd better get back to blowing up balloons," Al reminded them.

He handed long, thin balloons to Lottie and Mia, and took a round one for himself. He stretched the rubber as far as it would go, then blew and blew as hard as he could. It was working!

The balloon got **BIGGER, AND**

BIGGER AND . . .

AROOOOOOO! Einstein howled. **AROOOOOOOOOOOO!**

"Shhh!" Filip told him. "You are so loud. They will hear you next door."

"I don't want anyone upsetting the Goods again," Mum sighed. "Or their cat."

"Nor do we!" Al and Lottie said together. It wasn't that long since they had got into trouble with their next door neighbours, Mr and Mrs Good, and their cat, Precious. They'd experimented to see if it would be possible to waterproof the capsule of a time machine. Everything had ended up a bit wet!

The bell rang on the shop door that was connected to the Boffins' house. "I'll be back soon," Mum told them. "Don't eat the cake mix. I'll get it in the oven when I come back."

Lottie and Mia both struggled to tie a

knot at the end of their long balloons. It made the rubber squeak. Einstein stared at them suspiciously.

Suddenly, Mia's balloon shot out of her hands.

THPPPPTH! It zipped around the room, making a squelchy, squealing noise.

"That's the sound Einstein's bottom sometimes makes!" Lottie giggled. She held her balloon in the air.

PPPPPTH! It whizzed off too.

"This is fun!" Mia quickly blew up another round balloon and let it go.

PHTHHHHPPPPP!

Einstein yapped excitedly as he chased deflating balloons around the kitchen.

WOOF!

WOOF! WOOF!

"Wow!" Al exclaimed. "The sudden rush of air makes the balloons go really fast." He looked thoughtful. "That's the sort of thrust and acceleration I would need to get my time machine going."

"What time machine?" asked Filip.

"The one I'm inventing," Al said, seriously.

"Your mother would like to travel back in time, I think," Filip said.

"Exactly! She was happier when Dad was alive," Al told him. "Lottie's been helping me design one. We've experimented to find the shape of the time-machine capsule and how to protect it when it splashes down to Earth on water. I've been looking at Grandpa Boffin's books, and the only way to travel in time is to make the time machine go at the speed of light . . ."

AWESOME FACTS:
THE SPEED OF LIGHT

The fastest known speed in the universe is the speed of light. Scientists agree that the speed of light is 299,792,458 metres per second – that's like circling the Earth seven and a half times a second.

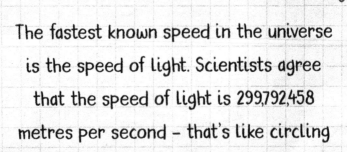

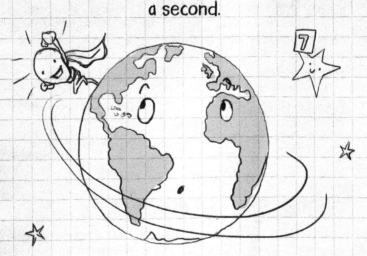

It takes about eight minutes and twenty seconds for the light from the Sun to reach Earth.

Einstein (the genius, not the dog) thought that time slows down the faster you go.

Scientists think that if you travel at the speed of light, you won't age at all. So if your time machine goes at the speed of light, you could return to Earth at any time in the future and not be any older.

If you think that's mind-boggling, you're right. Even scientists' minds are boggled when it comes to working out how to travel back in time, as that goes against all currently known laws of physics.

"Cool!" Mia exclaimed. "You'd need a tremendous amount of thrust to travel at the speed of light . . ."

"What is thrust?" Filip asked.

"Thrust is the force that's the result of the sudden release of stored energy," Al explained. "Energy was stored in the stretched sides of the balloons. It was suddenly released when we let them go. It's even stronger when you pop a balloon."

Mia's eyes shone. "You'd need a googolplex of balloons all popping at once to launch a full-sized time machine!" she exclaimed.

"How many are in a googolplex?" Al asked excitedly. "We might be able to do it!"

"A googolplex is a one followed by so many zeros that even a computer couldn't write them all down in a lifetime," Mia told him.

"Maybe we should just finish blowing up these balloons for your party," Filip said, picking up another balloon. "How are we going to put them up?"

Al grabbed a balloon and started rubbing it on his woolly jumper.

"Static electricity!" he grinned, holding the balloon against the wall.

The balloon clung to the wall as if it had been glued there. They watched as it gradually slid down the wall.

"We'll have to stick them up with sticky tape as usual," Lottie said. "But first, we need to blow them all up."

AWESOME FACT:
STATIC ELECTRICITY

Static electricity is the build-up of an electrical charge on the surface of an object – or even you. It can make things stick together – or push them apart.

Does your hair stand on end, or do you see sparks when you take off a jumper? That's static electricity – and so is lightning!

Soon everyone's cheeks were flushed. Al pulled off his jumper. "I'm running out of puff," he panted. He glanced at the ingredients next to Mum's mixing bowl. "There's another way to inflate balloons," he said. "It's awesomely scientific! We just need to borrow a bit of this baking powder — and one other ingredient."

Al rummaged in the cupboard and took out a bottle of vinegar. "It won't take long," he said confidently. "And Mum'll never even notice if we clear up the mess . . ."

Eruptions

Einstein sat and scratched, and Lottie, Mia and Filip watched as Al took a new balloon out of the bag and held it over Mrs Boffin's cake mix.

"It won't matter if a bit more baking powder goes into the mix," he said, spooning the powder into the neck of the balloon.

"That is not a bit more baking

powder," Filip said. "That is a lot."

"Oh, well, it'll just make Mum's sponge cake extra light and airy! It won't hurt anyone," Al replied.

Lottie quickly gave the cake mix a good stir to hide the extra baking powder.

Al put down the balloon and accidentally knocked over the tub of baking powder. "Ooops!" he said, and absent-mindedly scraped the heap of spilled baking powder into the open bag of icing sugar. Next, he unscrewed the lid of the vinegar bottle. "This will cause a mega chemical reaction!" he grinned.

Being careful not to let any baking

powder drop out of the balloon, Al fitted its neck over the top of the vinegar bottle.

"Time to experiment!" Al lifted the balloon so the baking powder fell into the vinegar.

WHOOOSH!

The mixture instantly turned to foam and fizzed up into the balloon.

"It works!" Filip cheered as the balloon began to inflate. He aimed the camera.

CLICK!

The balloon popped off the top of the bottle with a sticky **PLOP!** Instead of shooting off round the room, it

CLICK!

lay on the counter with foamy goo oozing out of it.

"It might not be the best way

to inflate a balloon," Al commented, "but that chemical reaction was awesome!"

"It's still going," Lottie said, as sticky foam plopped onto the kitchen floor.

It stank really strongly of vinegar. Einstein scampered over to take a look.

GAAAK! he spluttered, curling his lips. He took a big drink of water from his bowl, slunk back into the corner and resumed scratching.

"It's a bit like lava flowing out of a volcano . . ." Al muttered. "Hey, maybe if I put my time machine on top of a volcano it would have enough power to launch it!"

"Destroy it, more like," Lottie said. "A big volcanic eruption helped cause the extinction of the dinosaurs. But it would be really cool if a dinosaur was sitting on a volcano when it erupted and was blasted forward in time!'

"I like this idea," said Filip, "but I am thinking the dinosaur would be toast. What are you thinking, Mia?"

Mia was staring at the ceiling.

"I'm thinking we would need millions of tons of baking powder and an ocean of vinegar to launch a time machine with a chemical reaction like this!" she said.

"Imagine how much mess that would make . . ." Filip gasped. "We'd better clear this up for your mum," he told them.

"You're right!" Lottie agreed, handing him the mop.

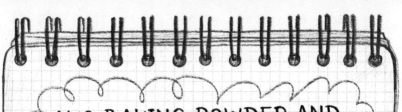

AL'S BAKING POWDER AND VINEGAR EXPERIMENT

To find out if you can inflate a balloon without blowing into it.

What Al used:

1 balloon

2 heaped teaspoons
baking powder

250 ml bottle of vinegar
that was half-full

What Al did:

He spooned the baking
powder into the balloon.

He took the lid off the
vinegar bottle.

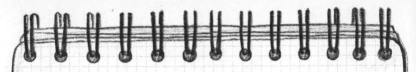

He fitted the balloon over the neck of the bottle, being careful not to let the baking powder drop into the bottle.

He lifted the balloon and let the baking powder drop into the bottle.

Results:

When the baking powder combined with the vinegar, the mixture fizzed and bubbled and the balloon began to inflate.

Observations

1. The mixture of the baking powder with the vinegar caused a chemical reaction that produced a gas called carbon dioxide, or CO_2. The gas inflated the balloon.

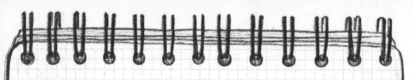

2. It would have been easier to get the baking powder into the balloon with a funnel.

3. It would be more scientific to use an empty bottle and measure 100 ml of vinegar into it.

4. This created a lot of stinky, sticky, vinegary goo, so it would have been a good idea to do the experiment in the sink or outside.

Try it at home! What will you discover?
WARNING: ASK A GROWN-UP FIRST!
It could get messy!

Al put the empty vinegar bottle in the recycling bin and opened the window to get rid of the vinegary smell. "We can't make a chemical reaction big enough to make a time machine go at the speed of light," he said thoughtfully. "We need another way to blast off. Time machines need a sudden burst of energy so they can jump through time . . ."

"There are plenty of animals that can jump," Lottie said. "Kangaroos for example, and frogs. They're sort of spring-loaded. The most powerful is the mantis shrimp . . ."

LOTTIE'S AWESOME ANIMAL FACT:
The peacock mantis shrimp

The peacock mantis shrimp (Odontodactylus scyllarus) has the world's fastest-moving limb. It can bash its prey with explosive speed and has been known to break the thick glass that is used for aquariums.

"Then there's octopus and squid. They blast off using jets of water," Lottie went on. "And then there's . . ."

She trailed off and stared at Einstein.

"Einstein?" Al sounded puzzled. "Einstein doesn't have blast-off powers. All he's doing is scratching."

"He's been scratching all day," Lottie said. "He must have fleas!"

Spring Loaded

Lottie wrestled Einstein to the ground. He lay there with his tail thumping on the tiles as Lottie searched through his fur.

"I hope Einstein doesn't have fleas," Al said. "Fleas are disgusting!"

Mia nodded in agreement. "Fleas lay eggs. If one flea lays two eggs, then they hatch and lay two eggs, and

so on, then in less than a month there are more than a billion fleas!"

"Wow! Fleas are pretty awesome!" Filip sounded impressed.

"Did you know that fleas have been around for millions of years. They could even bite their way through dinosaur skin!" Lottie said.

Al shuddered. Lottie was always full of wildlife facts, because she wanted to be a TV presenter when she grew up.

FRIGHTFUL FLEA FACTS
(try saying that quickly!)

Fleas can lay up to 50 eggs a day in animal fur, but the eggs are not very sticky, so they mostly drop off. Fleas drink blood. They poop dried blood, which the flea larvae feed on.

"I don't want to get bitten!" Al watched nervously as Lottie parted Einstein's fur. A tiny insect scuttled along the parting and back into the furry jungle.

"Yep, Einstein has a flea!" Lottie said matter-of-factly.

"**EEEK!**" Al shrieked. He backed into a corner and began checking himself for fleas. Einstein jumped to his feet and ran up to him, tail wagging.

"It's not a game!" Al squeaked, leaping away from him. Einstein's tail wagged as he scampered around him.

"Nice dance moves!" Lottie giggled

Mia doubled over with laughter.

Filip grabbed the camera.

CLICK! CLICK! CLICK!

Lottie wiped the tears of laughter from her eyes.

"Einstein, out!" she commanded, pointing to the garden door.

Einstein's ears drooped as he trotted outside.

"Oh dear! He does not know what it is he has done wrong," Filip said.

"Don't worry," Lottie said, "he's already forgotten about it. For a dog with the name of a genius, he doesn't have a very big brain." She pointed out the window. "Look! He's quite happy snuffling around the garden."

"We mustn't forget to tell Mum, so

she can treat him with flea medicine," Al said. "We don't want fleas jumping around all over the place."

"Fleas can jump up to 40 centimetres," Lottie said. "That's more than 150 times their own height. Their legs are like catapults."

"Catapults . . ." Al grinned. It was as if a lightbulb had gone off in his head. "Maybe we could catapult the time machine to launch it back in time!"

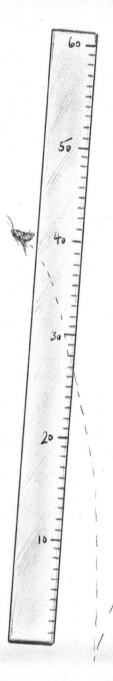

"You would be needing an army of fleas to catapult a time machine!" Filip said.

"You can train fleas," Lottie giggled. "There are flea circuses! Imagine all those creepy crawlies. You'd love that, Al!"

Al was too fired up with his idea even to shudder at the thought. "We can create flea energy without fleas," he said excitedly. "It's time for a new experiment! Let's make a catapult. No, let's make four catapults and have a catapult competition! We need a wooden spoon each, a kitchen roll and some elastic bands . . ."

"I know where those are." Lottie rushed off and came back with a handful of elastic bands.

Al was busy handing out wooden spoons and kitchen rolls. They watched carefully as he demonstrated how to use the elastic bands to fix the spoons to the kitchen rolls.

"Now, what can we use to test them? Oh, I know . . ." Al spotted a pack of mini marshmallows. He gave everyone a handful.

"Let's go outside and see how far we can ping them!" he said.

They took it in turns to twang their catapults.

Marshmallows whizzed all over the garden and even over the fence!

Einstein pricked his ears and scampered about, gobbling them up.

"It's hard to know where the marshmallows will go," Al observed. "And these marshmallows are very light. I'm not sure it's possible to make a big enough catapult to launch a time machine . . ."

"Probably not. But Einstein thinks this is a great game." Filip giggled.

AL, LOTTIE, MIA AND FILIP'S WOODEN SPOON CATAPULT EXPERIMENT

To see if energy stored in a wooden spoon catapult will provide thrust to launch marshmallows into the air.

What they used for each person:

1 wooden spoon

1 kitchen roll

3 large elastic bands
(If you, only have small ones, take the paper off the kitchen roll.)

Mini marshmallows

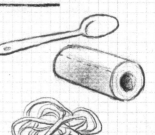

Yum!

What they each did:

They laid the spoon across the middle of the kitchen roll.

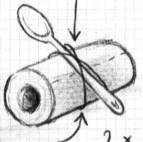

They criss-crossed two elastic bands over the spoon handle to hold it in place on the roll.

2 x elastic bands

They looped the third elastic band over the neck of the spoon, around the back of the roll and over the handle end of the spoon.

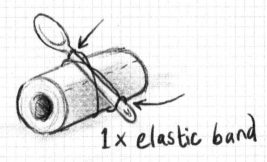

1 x elastic band

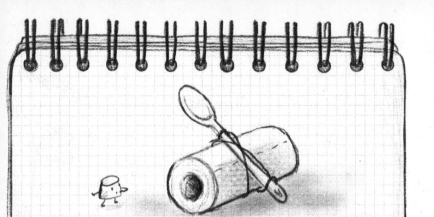

They adjusted the roll and spoon so that the bottom of the spoon handle rested on the ground and the spoon was pointing upwards.

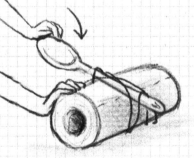

Holding the kitchen roll steady, they pulled the top of the spoon downwards.

They put a marshmallow on the spoon, and let go.

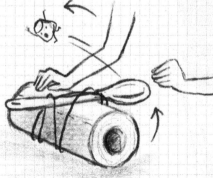

Results:

The marshmallows
were catapulted
everywhere.

Observations:

1. Stretching the elastic bands by pulling down
   on the spoon stored energy in them. Scientists
   call stored energy potential energy.

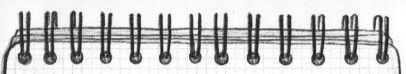

2. When the spoon was let go, the potential energy stored in the rubber bands was transferred to the spoon - and onto the marshmallows.

3. The sudden release of potential energy provided the thrust that made the marshmallows fly off the spoon.

4. It is very hard to judge where marshmallows will land.

Try it at home! What will you discover?
WARNING: ASK A GROWN-UP FIRST!
It could get messy!

"Come on, let's see what else we can ping with the catapults!" said Al heading back inside. He nearly collided with Mum at the back door.

"What are you up to?" she asked, looking suspiciously at the spoons

attached to kitchen rolls.

"We've just finished an experiment," Al told her.

"An experiment? I can't see much mess!" Mum exclaimed in surprise. "Can you all stay out of the kitchen please? I'm in a hurry to get the cake in the oven."

"OK," Al said. He lowered his voice. "I have another idea to test out."

"What is it?" Lottie whispered, as Mum went back inside.

"We need something really powerful to launch a time machine," Al said. "Something like a rocket!"

Blast-off!

"I saw this experiment in one of Great Grandpa Boffin's books," he told Lottie, Mia and Filip. "We just need a plastic bottle with water in it, a cork, a bike pump, a needle adaptor for blowing up footballs . . ."

Al rushed about, gathering the things he needed for his experiment on the garden table. Once he had assembled them, he took the needle adaptor and pushed it all the way through the cork. He then fitted the cork into the neck of the bottle.

"Let's add some wings and a nose," he said, "so it will look like a real rocket."

"Now, I need a way to hold the bottle in an upside-down position," he said.

"Can you use the middle of the table?" Lottie asked, pointing out the hole where the parasol fitted.

"Perfect!" Al tipped the bottle upside down so its neck went through the hole. Then he crawled under the table and connected the bike pump to the needle adaptor.

"Stand back!' he warned everyone. "It'll go off without any warning."

Filip got ready with the camera.

Al made sure the bottle was upright, and pumped madly.

There was a sudden **WHOOSH!**

"BLAST-OFF!"

Al cried.

The rocket blasted off from the cork and whizzed into the sky on a jet of air and water!

"WOW!" everyone gasped in awe.

CLICK! Filip got a shot of it as it flew up even higher than the roof! Then, all of a sudden, the rocket began to fall . . .

"Oh no, it's going to hit the Goods' roof," Lottie groaned. "It's heading for their chimney! What if it knocks it off?"

The twins held their breath and waited for the crash. The rocket disappeared.

"What happened to it?" Filip asked.

Al's face had gone pale under his freckles.

"It must have gone down the Goods' chimney," he gasped.

There was a high-pitched

YEEE-OOOWL!

from next door. Al, Lottie, Filip and

Mia raced to the fence and peered over.

Mrs Good rushed out of her house, carrying a very grubby-looking cat.

"Precious!" she wailed. "Your beautiful fur is covered in soot! Mumsie will need to clean you up!" Mrs Good glared suspiciously at the twins.

"Precious was sleeping on the carpet in front of our old fireplace when suddenly soot billowed out all over the place." Mrs Good glowered. "Did it have anything to do with you?"

"Er, it might have had something to

do with our bottle rocket going down your chimney . . ." Al sighed.

"We're very sorry," Lottie added. "It was an accident."

"Very, very sorry," Al echoed.

"It was a totally freak accident," Mia told her. "I estimate there was less than a zero point zero zero one percent chance of it happening even if we had tried aiming it down your chimney!"

"A freak accident? **LOOK AT THE STATE OF US!**" Mrs Good snarled, clutching Precious to her bosom. Her blouse was getting covered in soot too. "I'll have to talk to your mother about cleaning bills — not to mention sweeping the chimney and extracting that bottle . . ."

"I understand that you are cross,"

said Filip. "But perhaps you could be cross tomorrow? Today, it is the twins' birthday. It was their Dad's birthday, too!"

"That's right," Al confirmed. He glanced at Lottie. She nodded.

"And we would love it if you and Mr Good could come to our party this afternoon and have a piece of birthday cake," she said quickly.

The twins put on their politest smiles. Mrs Good seemed to be lost for words.

"Did someone say birthday cake?" Mr Good appeared beside his wife.

"Nothing nicer than a piece of birthday cake, I always say. We would love to come, wouldn't we, Mildred?"

"Errr . . . um . . . yes, I suppose we could . . ." Mrs Good muttered. "I've been waiting for an occasion to wear my new outfit. I'll call the hairdresser and tell him I need to see him right now . . ."

"That's settled then." Mr Good smiled. "Happy birthday! We'll see you later."

"It will be such fun!" Filip laughed. "I can't wait!"

AL'S BOTTLE ROCKET EXPERIMENT

To see if water and pressurised air will provide enough power to make a bottle blast off like a rocket.

What Al used:

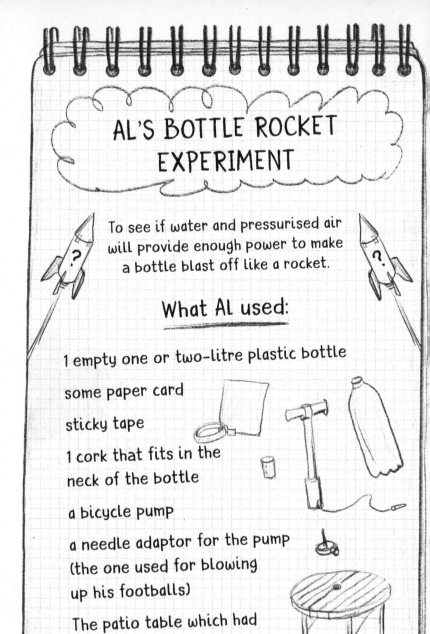

1 empty one or two-litre plastic bottle

some paper card

sticky tape

1 cork that fits in the neck of the bottle

a bicycle pump

a needle adaptor for the pump (the one used for blowing up his footballs)

The patio table which had a hole in it for a parasol*

What Al did:

He carefully pushed the needle adaptor through the cork.**

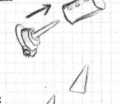

He cut out four fins and a cone from the card and taped them onto the bottle.

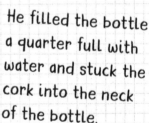

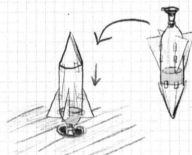

He filled the bottle a quarter full with water and stuck the cork into the neck of the bottle.

He placed the bottle upside down in the parasol hole.

He connected the pump to the needle adaptor.

---

*If you don't have an outdoor table, you could fill a bucket with damp sand and scoop out a hole to prop up the bottle.

**You may need to ask a grown-up to help with this. If the needle adaptor's not long enough to go through the cork, get them to cut the cork in half for you.)

Al pumped like crazy for a few seconds until the rocket took off.

Results:

The cork suddenly popped out of the bottle rocket, sending it high into the air, propelled by a jet of air and water.

AIR + WATER
PUSH DOWN

Try it at home! What will you discover? WARNING: ASK A GROWN-UP FIRST! It could get messy! Do this experiment outside. The rocket will take off very suddenly.

Observations:

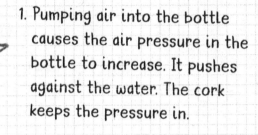

1. Pumping air into the bottle causes the air pressure in the bottle to increase. It pushes against the water. The cork keeps the pressure in.

UPWARDS THRUST

2. When the pressure gets too great for the cork to stay in the bottle, it pops out.

3. The air and water inside jet downwards out of the bottle. This thrusts the bottle upwards.

 WARNING: Keep spectators at a safe distance. Once you have started pumping, make sure the bottle rocket is ALWAYS pointing away from you.

5

Big Burp

"Ta-da!" Mum plonked a bright green birthday cake dusted with icing sugar in the middle of the living room table. It had the symbol of an atom iced on top with a tiny T-Rex sitting in the middle. "I'm very pleased with how it turned out. It's

the lightest, airiest sponge I've ever made . . ."

"That'll be the extra baking powder," Al whispered in Lottie's ear.

"The green icing and the dinosaur is for Lottie, and the atom design is for Al," Mrs Boffin explained. "There's jam in the middle and I was going to put tiny marshmallows on it, too, but I couldn't find any. I was sure I had a bag of them."

"We prefer it without them," Lottie said hurriedly.

"It looks great, Mum, thanks!' Al agreed, beaming from ear to ear.

Al was having an awesome birthday. The new socks that Mr and Mrs Good had given them weren't very exciting, but the other presents were brilliant! Mum had bought them both new scooters. It was going to be fun, learning to perform stunts on them . . . Filip had given Lottie a cool take-apart anatomy model of a dinosaur and Mia's gift to him was glow-in-the dark face paint and a torch that he couldn't wait to try out.

"I'm sure the cake will be delicious!" Mr Good rubbed his hands together.

Mrs Good took her handbag off

her lap and put it down on the floor. "I don't want any sticky green icing or jammy fingers on my nice new handbag!" she said.

Mum lit the candle. "Are you ready to take a family photo, Filip?" she asked.

"I am," Filip confirmed.

Mrs Good patted her hair. It looked as if it was set solid with hairspray. "I'm so glad the hairdresser could fit me in," she told her husband. "I hate to look untidy in photos."

"Hold on a moment!" Mum exclaimed. "There's someone missing."

Al and Lottie instantly thought of their dad.

"Of course, you must take a moment to remember Mr Boffin," Filip said.

"We'll never, ever forget him," Mum said, exchanging a sad little smile with the twins. "But I was thinking of another family member who can be here . . ."

She rushed to the door and let in Einstein. Before Al or Lottie could mention that he might still have fleas, Mum led everyone into singing 'Happy Birthday!'

Lottie glanced at Al. "The fleas

probably jumped off in the garden," she whispered. "We'll tell her later."

Al nodded. "Count to three, then blow out the candle?" he grinned.

Everyone joined in.

"One, two, three!"

The twins blew out the candle.
PHHHFF!

"Make a wish!" Mum smiled.

"Say cheese!" called Filip.
CLICK!

Filip passed the camera to Mrs Boffin so she could see the photo. "That is a good one!" Mum exclaimed happily. "I'll have to get it framed."

"May I see?" asked Mrs Good. Mum handed her the camera.

"Oh, that is a nice photo." Mrs Good turned to Filip. "Perhaps you could take one of me in my new outfit?"

"Sure!" Filip said, taking back the camera. **CLICK!**

Mrs Boffin cut the cake.

"I bet I know what you wished for!" Lottie told Al, as Mum handed round slices.

"I bet I know what you wished, too!" Al said.

The twins, Mia and Filip nibbled cautiously at their cake. They looked at one another.

"It tastes a bit funny," Lottie whispered.

"Must be the extra baking powder," Al agreed.

When no-one was looking, all four of them secretly held their slices under the table. Einstein soon gobbled up the cake and licked crumbs off their fingers with his warm, wet tongue.

Mr and Mrs Good didn't seem to notice. They were enthusiastically forking cake into their mouths.

"I say!" Mr Good gave a little burp. "I have a tiny bit of wind."

A look of shock crossed Mrs Good's face. "Do try to mind your manners, dear," she hissed at her husband.

Mr Good finished his large piece of cake and brushed crumbs off his shirt.

"URPPPP!"

he burped. Mrs Good looked outraged.

"Please excuse me," Mr Good said apologetically.

"It can't be the baking powder," Al whispered. "It wouldn't cause that sort of reaction after it was cooked."

Mr Good gave another, louder belch. "That's better!" he sighed.

"You scooped baking powder into the icing sugar," Lottie groaned.

"Did I?" Al sounded surprised. "But that still wouldn't react once it was made into icing."

"Mum dusted that icing sugar on top of the cake!" Lottie said.

"That'd do it!" Al stared at Mrs Good. She was hitching about on her seat, looking very uncomfortable. She tapped her chest with her fist.

"She's trying not to burp!" Lottie gasped.

Mrs Good pursed her lips. She was going red in the face. She bent down, took a handkerchief out of her bag and pressed it to her mouth.

"It's no good," she said in a muffled voice. "I have to let it out . . ."

Mrs Good's burp rumbled around the room.

UUUUUR PPPPPP!

"Oh   dear!"   Mum   exclaimed.
"Something has made you both burp.
I wonder what it could be? You two
didn't add anything to the cake, did
you?" she asked the twins.

Lottie attempted to look innocent.

Al went for an expression of
hurt surprise.

"A bit of extra baking powder may have accidentally got in," Al murmured.

Mum raised her eyebrows.

"A little bit extra baking powder and a few tiny burps is nothing to worry about," said Mr Good. "I'd like another slice, please." He held out his plate.

UUUUURP! he burped. "Sorry, Mildred!"

"I have some mints in my handbag," Mrs Good said. "We should all have one to settle our tummies!"

She passed round a bag of smooth, round white mints with chewy centres.

Al popped one in his mouth and

took a sip of cola. The mix of cola and mint was really tasty, but there was something else happening, too. Gassy foam fizzed and bubbled on the back of his tongue. He swallowed.

HIC! HIC! HIC!

Al hiccupped.

"What's going on?" Mia asked him.

"Not-**HIC**-sure," Al said. "I need to experiment to find out!"

Explosive Ending

"It's some-**HIC**-thing, to . . . **HIC!** Do with mints and cola!" Al took a deep breath. "Do you have any more mints, Mrs Good?" he said in a rush.

"Well . . . since it's your birthday, I suppose you can have some more." Mrs Good bent down, opened her handbag and handed Al the whole packet.

"Thank you! Time to . . . **HIC!** Experiment. Come on!" Al jumped to his feet and led Lottie, Mia and Filip to the corner of the room.

At the table, Mum sighed contentedly. "I'm so pleased to see Al and Lottie and their friends taking such an interest in science," she told Mr and Mrs Good. "And it's very nice to have you round for a cup of tea and a chat that isn't about the twins upsetting you!"

Al stood a new bottle of cola on the carpet, tipped the mints into the palm of his hand and unscrewed the cap.

"Count down from ten and I'll-**HIC!** Drop in the mints," Al said.

"10 . . . 9 . . . 8 . . . 7 . . . 6 . . . 5 . . . 4 . . . 3 . . . 2 . . . 1!" Mia, Filip and Lottie chorused.

Al dropped in the whole packet of mints. **"BLAST OFF!"** he yelled.

A fountain of cola rocketed upwards. Al, Lottie, Filip and Mia leaped out of the way.

"Wow!" Al gasped. "With that amount of thrust, a time machine really could blast off!" He was so surprised, his hiccups stopped.

AL'S FIZZY COLA EXPERIMENT

To see what happens if you drop mints into a bottle of cola.

What Al used:

1 litre bottle of cola (any sort)

1 packet of mints.*

* The sort of mint that is round and white with a chewy centre works best, any make. You need at least 15 normal-sized mints that will easily drop through the neck of the bottle.

What Al did:

He took the top off the cola bottle. He dropped in a whole packet of mints.

Results:

A fountain of foamy cola sprayed up as high as the ceiling.

Observations:

1. Fizzy drinks are made by adding pressurised carbon dioxide to water, then keeping the mix under pressure in a closed can or bottle. When mints are added, they react with the cola and release the carbon dioxide.

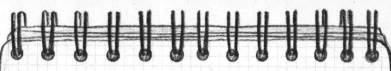

2. Gas bubbles gush out of the bottle, providing the thrust to launch the cola fountain.

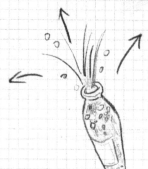

3. It would be easier to drop the mints in the bottle quickly, using a funnel of some kind (you could make one out of paper).

4. You'd get into a lot less trouble if you did this outside.

 Try it at home! What will you discover?
WARNING: ASK A GROWN-UP FIRST!
It could get messy!

"What just happened?" Mum gulped, as cola rained down on her and the Goods. They all stared at the ceiling.

"Uh-oh!" Al whispered. He nudged Lottie and pointed wordlessly to Mrs Good's new handbag. It was overflowing with brown, sticky foam.

"My bag! I forgot to shut it!" Mrs Good shrieked. She jumped to her feet and grabbed her ruined handbag. A balloon floated down from the wall and bounced off her hairsprayed helmet of hair.

Lottie couldn't help giggling.

CLICK!

Filip quickly snapped a photo.

One after another, balloons dripping with minty cola drifted down.

"Perhaps we should go, Mildred, dear." Mr Good took his wife by the elbow, but she seemed to be frozen to the spot, like Mrs Boffin. The twins' mum was gazing in open-mouthed consternation at the cola stains on Mrs Good's new outfit, the sofa and the carpet.

A balloon landed in front of Einstein. He grabbed it in his jaws and it exploded with a loud **BANG!**

Einstein went bonkers. He raced madly round and round the table chasing and snapping at balloons.

WOOF! WOOF! WOOF!

Filip pointed the camera at him:
CLICK! CLICK! CLICK!

"Come on, dear," Mr Good urged his wife, but she wasn't paying attention. She stepped right into Einstein's orbit and the over-excited dog collided with her.

WHUMP!

Mrs Good and Einstein ended up on the carpet in a damp, disheveled heap.

Mrs Good struggled to sit up. Al rushed to help, but before he could grab the dog's collar, Einstein sprang to his

feet, wagging his tail enthusiastically in Mrs Good's face. His bottom gave a sudden **PAAARP!** right next to her nose! She clutched at her throat and turned a delicate shade of green.

"Phew, that's a stinky one!" Al gagged.

Lottie, Mia and Filip all held their noses and nodded.

DISGUSTING FACT: FARTS

Farts are caused by trapped air escaping from the intestines. The stink is caused by sulphur gas, which is made when food is digested.

The noise is caused by the vibrations of the muscles in your bottom. The loudness depends on the tightness of these muscles and the speed of the air leaving the body.

Mrs Good sat on the floor, gasping like a fish out of water. Einstein peered worriedly into her face. He gave her nose a friendly, slurpy lick.

The twins watched in horrified fascination as a tiny brown insect leapt off Einstein — and landed in Mrs Good's hair.

"A flea!" Mrs Good howled.

She leaped to her feet and bounced round the living room, tearing at her newly-done hair. "Get it off, get it off, get it off me!

"NOWWW!!!"

Mia's eyes shone. "I've calculated something," she said. "This is the exact moment to blast off in a time machine!"

"Maybe this is the moment to stop your experimenting, Al?" Filip suggested.

"I'm a scientist, and scientists **NEVER** give up," Al said. "Everyone has times when they need a time machine." He looked around at the remains of the birthday tea, and the cross expressions on the faces of Mum and Mr and Mrs Good. "Especially me!"

AWESOME BLAST-OFF
FACT: THRUST

Thrust is the force created by the release
of potential energy. In Al's bottle rocket
experiment, potential energy is created by
compressing the air in the bottle. When
the energy is released, the rocket blasts
off on a jet of water and air. The direction
the rocket goes in is the opposite to
the direction of the blast.

This is an example of one of Sir
Isaac Newton's Laws of Motion:
For each action there is an
equal and opposite reaction.

BALLOON ROCKET EXPERIMENT

To show how thrust works.

What you will need:

1 balloon (a long one is best,
but any shape will do)
a bulldog clip
a long length of smooth, thin string
a paper straw
sticky tape

How to do the experiment:

1. Thread the string
   through the straw.

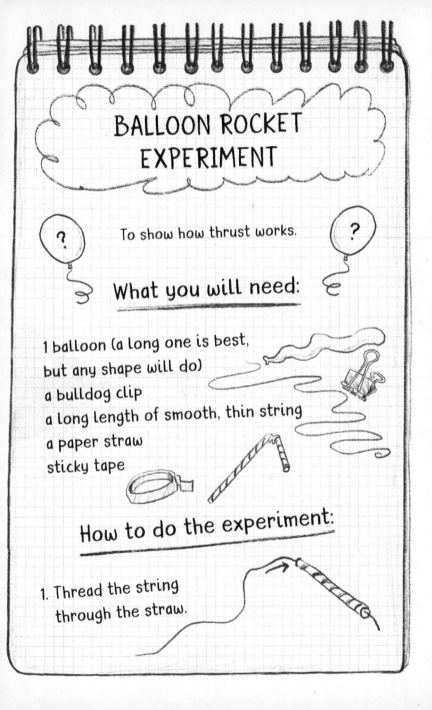

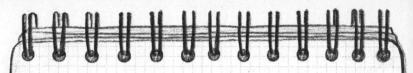

2. Tie one end of the string to a door handle and the other end to the back of a chair.

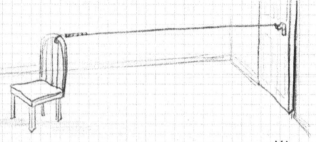

3. Move the chair away from the door until the string is tight.

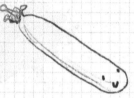

4. Blow up the balloon, twist the end and put the clip on it so the air doesn't escape.

5. Attach the balloon lengthwise to the straw using sticky tape, with the clip next to the chair.

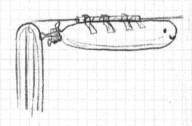

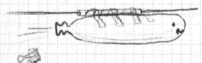

6. Take off the clip. Watch the balloon!

How it works:

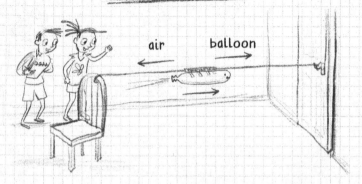

air   balloon

As the air rushes out, it propels the balloon in the opposite direction (like Newton's third law of motion says.) Because it is taped to the straw, the balloon goes in a straight line.

Why not try these variations:

1. Blow up the balloon by different amounts, then see how far it travels along the string.

2. Vary the height of the string attached to the chair to see what difference travelling up different slopes makes.

Read all of **AL'S AWESOME SCIENCE** adventures and have fun doing more experiments at home!

Al is experimenting to find the best shape for his time-machine capsule . . . with eggs! But a nosy neighbour and her cat Precious land him and his twin sister Lottie in a very sticky situation.

Al is experimenting to find out what kind of covering his time-machine capsule will need to survive its **SPLASH DOWN!** back to Earth. Trouble is, Al needs to borrow the neighbour's knickers and Mum's bucket. Can he get himself out of this wet mess before Mum finds out?